# We Should Do This More Often

Written and illustrated

by

Joan McCartney

Other books by the author:

*The Other Side Makes Chocolate*
   -A humorous look at breastfeeding and parenting through cartoons. 88 pages.

*Baby in the Making*
   -A nine-month journal for the mother-to-be. 80 pages.

First Printing June, 1987

ISBN   0-9609788-2-8

Published by:

Joan M. McCartney
21 South Auten Avenue
Somerville, New Jersey 08876

Dedicated to children everywhere,
especially those who wait for
their forever homes.

Thank you to all the parents and children whose delightful sayings and humorous family situations helped to fill the pages of this book. Thanks especially for the inspirations from my own family.

"THE 5:00 P.M. FANTASY"

YES, AUNT MARY, I LOVE THE PLAYPEN YOU SENT.
IT'S COMING IN VERY HANDY!

WOULD YOU MOVE YOUR STOMACH. THE BABY'S
KICKING IS KEEPING ME AWAKE.

YUP!

I'M AT THAT IN-BETWEEN STAGE OF PREGNANCY...
TOO SMALL FOR MATERNITY CLOTHES AND TOO
LARGE FOR MY REGULAR CLOTHES.

I DON'T MIND THE BOOTS,
BUT THE SPURS HAVE TO GO.

WHEN YOU EAT A SUB SANDWICH, WHY
IS THE TOP PIECE OF BREAD ALWAYS
GONE BEFORE THE BOTTOM PIECE?

I DON'T WANT TO CARRY THE BAG. IT'S NOT FAIR!
YOU ALWAYS MAKE ME CARRY EVERYTHING!

ARE THERE TOILETS IN HEAVEN?

HEY MOM, GUESS WHOSE CAR
JUST PULLED UP IN OUR DRIVEWAY?

EXCUSE ME LADY, I THINK YOUR BABY
JUST NEEDS A HUG.

IT'S HARD TO BELIEVE THE TWINS ARRIVED FROM
KOREA A YEAR AGO. DO YOU THINK SOMEDAY
YOU'LL TELL THEM THEY'RE ADOPTED?

PEEK-A-BOO!

I KNOW WHICH BATTERIES LAST THE LONGEST,
CAN YOU TELL ME WHICH ONES LAST THE SHORTEST?

15

I HAFTA GO TO THE BAFFROOM.

BUT THE DOCTOR SAID WE COULD
DO IT AFTER SIX WEEKS.

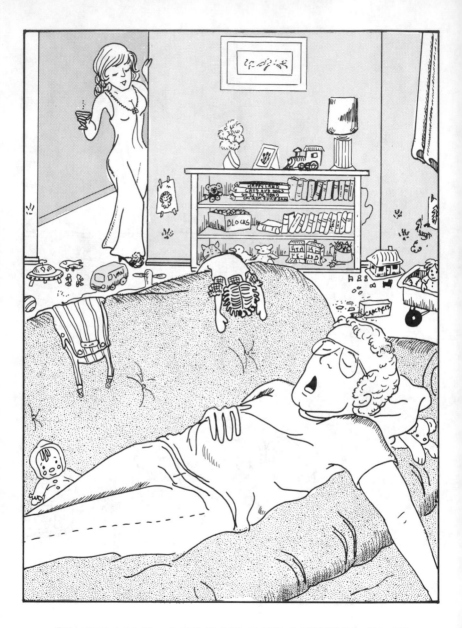

OH, WILLIAM...I WAS ABLE TO ACCOMPLISH SO
MANY THINGS TODAY WHILE YOU WATCHED THE
CHILDREN, AND NOW THAT THEY'RE ASLEEP...

YES, I HAVE A QUESTION. WHERE ARE
THE HOLES WHERE THEY SHOT THEM?

I'LL SHOW YOU MINE, THEN YOU SHOW ME YOURS.

21

HOW ARE YOU TEACHING THE OLDER CHILDREN
TO BE GENTLE WITH THE BABY?

NOW, WHERE DID I PUT MY GLASSES?

25

I'D PREFER YOU DIDN'T PLAY WITH GUNS, HONEY.

KA-CHOW! KA-CHOW! I GOT YOU!

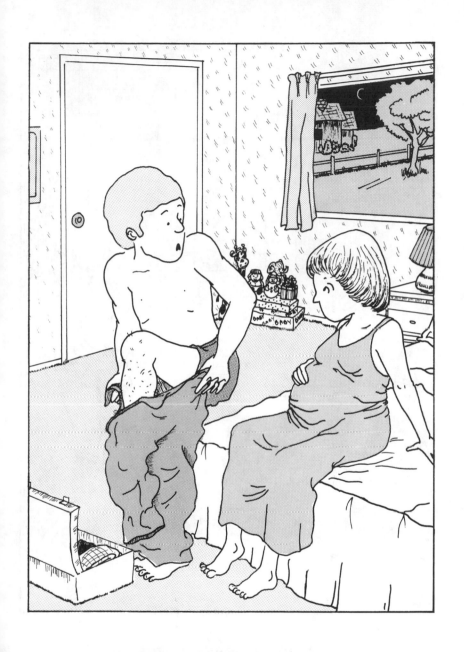

BUT IT'S NOT DUE UNTIL TUESDAY!

BUT MOM, THEY'RE CLEEEAN!
I'VE ONLY WORN THEM FOR FIVE DAYS!

THESE ARE THE ADAMS, OUR NEW NEIGHBORS. THEY ADOPTED JILL FROM INDIA AND TYLER FROM SOUTH AMERICA, BUT THEY DON'T HAVE ANY CHILDREN "OF THEIR OWN."

SORE, HUH?

KRISTIN, DID YOU SEE MOMMY'S
NEW PAIR OF PANTYHOSE?

YEAH, MY MOM IS ALWAYS NURSING MY BROTHER.
HE'S ON "COMMAND FEEDING."

DADDY, WHAT WAS IT LIKE IN THE
"GOOD OLD DAYS" WHEN YOU WERE A LITTLE BOY?

MY OCCUPATION?...MATERNAL PRACTITIONER.

IT'S OKAY, HONEY...SHE'S IN BED WITH US.

YOU'RE THE PRETTIEST MOMMY
IN THE WHOLE WIDE WORLD!

I HAD A NON-SLEEPER...YOU GET USED TO IT.
BY THE TIME MY YOUNGEST SLEPT THROUGH
THE NIGHT, MY OLDEST STARTED STAYING
OUT HALF THE NIGHT.

NOT THAT ONE! TAKE THE OTHER ONE OUT!

YOU'VE GOT TO BE KIDDING.

GRANDMA'S NOT WIPING YOUR KISS AWAY, HONEY.
I'M JUST RUBBING IT IN.

42

YES, NURSING A TODDLER IS DIFFERENT AND
VERY REWARDING. IT GIVES US SOME SPECIAL...
UM...QUIET...UHH...MOMENTS TOGETHER. OW!
WOULD YOU HOLD ON A MINUTE?

WALLET, CREDIT CARDS, DIAPER, TISSUE, LIP
GLOSS, BRUSH, RAISINS...I KNOW THE CAR KEYS
ARE IN HERE SOMEWHERE...

MOMMY, DO YOU THINK PEOPLE WILL KNOW
THAT I MADE YOUR MOTHER'S DAY HAT?

MOMMY, WHICH IS A BOY...
A MALE OR A FEMALE?

BUT I DID!
I DID PICK UP EVERYTHING OFF THE FLOOR.

MOMMY, THEY HAVE BIG TOILETS IN THE MAN'S
BAFFROOM...AND THEY'RE ON THE WALL!
WANNA COME SEE?!

TAKE THEM BACK TO THE GARAGE.
THE KIDS ARE STILL AWAKE.

PHONE CALLS, HAIR DRYERS, VCR'S, FOOD,
SHAMPOO, SNEAKERS, JEANS...AND I USED TO
THINK THE DIAPER YEARS WERE EXPENSIVE!

WHAT DO YOU MEAN,
THE BABY'S "FINGER PAINTING" IN THE CRIB?

WHAT DOES FATHER NATURE DO?

HE'S GOT UNCLE TODD'S EARS, AND AMANDA'S EYES, SEAN'S NOSE, SHANA'S MOUTH, CAM'S CHIN, JAYNE'S HANDS...

55

I FWUSHED!

I THINK I'VE GOT IT!

I DROPPED YOUR TOOTHBRUSH IN THE TOILET
THIS MORNING. BUT I RINSED IT OFF.

DID YOU EVER MEET
A PRINCE CHARMING, MOMMY?

WHICH ONE DID WE BUY?

MY BACKGROUND IS KOREAN.
MY FRONTGROUND IS AMERICAN.

DADDY PUT THE LAUNDRY AWAY AGAIN,
DIDN'T HE?

YES...(YAWN)...OF COURSE YOU CAN COME INTO
BED WITH US...BUT PLEASE...TONIGHT
GO TO THE BATHROOM FIRST.

MOM! DAD! WE'RE AHEAD...72 TO 56!

I'M ALL FINISHED.
YOU CAN TURN IT OFF AND PUT IT AWAY NOW.

OKAY, CONTRACTION ENDS. CONTRACTION ENDS...
UH, HONEY, IT'S SUPPOSED TO END NOW.

HI DADDY! WE'RE HELPING MOMMY
WAP CWISMUS GIFFS!

MOMMY, THE ARROW SAYS IT'S HUNGRY,
BUT IT WON'T SWALLOW MY MONEY.

AT NIGHT THE SUN GOES TO BED BEHIND THE
CLOUDS. IT GETS SO HOT BACK THERE THAT
THE MOON AND STARS HAVE TO COME OUT.

NOT ONLY IS EMILY NAPPING TODAY, BUT I WAS ABLE
TO FINISH WRAPPING THE CHRISTMAS GIFTS. IT'S SO
NICE TO BE ON SCHEDULE FOR A CHANGE,
EVEN IF IT DOSEN'T LAST.

I'M GLAD I'M FIVE!
I GET TO BE FIVE FOR A WHOLE YEAR!

...I DIDN'T KNOW SHE KNEW HOW TO USE SCISSORS.

OOOH!
OOOH! I KNOW!
I KNOW THE NAME OF
THE PILGRIM'S BOAT!

THE CAULIFLOWER!

BABY JESUS IS IN THE CRIB,
AND THAT'S HIS MOTHER AND FATHER,
MARY CHRISTMAS AND ROUN' JOHN VERSION.

WHICH IS THE ONE THAT DIED?

"...ARBOR PUBLIC SCHOOLS, BAYVILLE ELEMENTARY
SCHOOL, BRIDGETOWN BORO SCHOOLS,
CRANBURY PUBLIC SCHOOLS..."

BUT HIM CAN'T NURSE HIS TEDDY.
HIM'S NOT A BEAR.

SO, I HEAR BRANDON HAS MADE SOME
MODIFICATIONS TO HIS WHEELCHAIR.

I HAVEN'T SPENT A FULL NIGHT IN BED SINCE SHE'S ARRIVED. I GET UP TO GET HER WHEN SHE WAKES UP, AND I GET UP TO CHECK HER WHEN SHE DOESN'T!

WHOEVER SAID KISSES AREN'T FATTENING?

YOU SKIP THE SAME LINES
DADDY ALWAYS SKIPS, POPPY.

YEAH, BUT I SAW THE TOOTH FAIRY LAST NIGHT.
SHE'S TALL, WEARS PAJAMAS, AND HAS A BEARD.

BOY, GOD'S GONNA BE RICH!

YEAH, YOU SAID DON'T DUMP THE CEREAL OUT
TO GET AT THE PRIZES. WE DIDN'T.

MY MOMMY CAN'T COME TO THE PHONE RIGHT NOW.
SHE'S SHOWIN' HER EROTIC DANCIN'
TO THE NEIGHBOR NEXT DOOR.

OH, YEAH, I FORGOT.
RUSSELL WAS PLAYING WITH THE CLOCK RADIO...

WHEN YOU READ ALL THOSE BABY BOOKS WHILE
YOU'RE WAITING, YOUR BABY SEEMS LIKE A FAIRY
TALE. ONCE THE BABY'S HERE, SOME OF THOSE
BOOKS SEEM LIKE FAIRY TALES!

HEY, DAD, IS VIRGIN SPELLED WITH A "J" OR A "G"?

MY MOTHER IS A CHILDBIRTH INSTRUCTOR AND SHE
SAYS THERE ARE TWO WAYS FOR A BABY TO BE BORN:
THE VIRGINAL WAY AND BY SIBERIAN SESSION.

GOOD, HUH!

DO YOU HEAR ANY JINGLE BELLS YET?

WHO, HIM?
THAT'S JUST MY BROTHER.

MY SISTER AND I GOT BORNED TWO TIMES: ONCE
NAKED AND ONCE WITH CLOTHES ON...
THATS WHEN WE GOT ADOPTED.

YOU'RE IN GOOD HANDS...HE'S AN EXCELLENT DOCTOR
AND EASY TO WORK WITH. I'VE SPENT A NUMBER
OF YEARS TRAINING HIM MYSELF.

MOM...WORMS DON'T TASTE GOOD.

THIS IS THE BEST PART, GRANDPA...WHERE THE
SPACE MONSTERS EAT THE DEAD BODIES WITH THE
REMOTE CONTROL DEVICES. WAIT'LL YA SEE THEM
GET BLASTED INTO SPACE! AWESOME!

IT ALWAYS STOPS
WHEN I CALL YOU INTO THE ROOM.

I HEARD A NEW JOKE YESTERDAY, GRAMA.
WHY DID THE CHICKEN CROSS THE ROAD?

IT DOESN'T MATTER WHO GOES FIRST, DADDY,
SO I'LL GO FIRST.

WHY DO BABIES HAVE TO BREATHE SO QUIETLY?

DADDY SAYS THIS BOOK IS ABOUT THE
PRINCE OF WALES, BUT I CAN'T FIND
ANY PICTURES OF ANY WHALES!

IF YOU GIVE ME A COOKIE,
I'LL BE YOUR BEST FRIEND.

AHHH, THE SHEETS ARE ON THE LINE, THE REST OF THE LAUNDRY IS FOLDED, THE PLACE IS PICKED UP...I ACTUALLY HAVE A FEW MINUTES TO SIT DOWN.

WE WERE JUST PRETENDING TO BE BLIND,
LIKE JULIE. BOY IS SHE GOOD AT
WALKING AROUND IN THE DARK!

HAVING A VCR HAS ONE MAJOR DRAWBACK:
WHEN I WANT TO STAY UP LATER TO WATCH
SOMETHING, MY PARENTS TELL ME
TO TAPE IT AND GO TO BED.

MOMMY, DID YOU NURSE THE BABY ONLY ON ONE SIDE,
OR DID YOU FORGET TO BUCKLE UP?

YOU SAID WE COULD HAVE TWO PIECES OF CANDY; DOES THAT
MEAN TWO LARGE PIECES OR TWO SMALL? CAN ONE LARGE
EQUAL THREE SMALL PIECES? HOW MANY PIECES DOES A
LOLLYPOP EQUAL? IS A ROLL OF MINTS LARGE OR MEDIUM?
CAN WE HAVE FOUR HALVES OF FOUR PIECES TO EQUAL...

IT WASN'T THAT LONG AGO WHEN BIG BIRD WAS
HER IDOL AND I WAS HER BOYFRIEND.

MAMA, YOU SAID THIS WAS GOD'S HOUSE...
SO WHERE DOES GOD SLEEP?

HOW MANY TIMES DO I HAVE TO TELL YOU? YOU
HAVE TO ASK FIRST IF YOU WANT TO PLAY WITH PAPA'S
TOOLS. AND THEN YOU HAVE TO PUT THEM AWAY WHEN
YOU'RE DONE! YOU JUST DON'T LISTEN, DO YOU?

YOU'LL LEARN ONE RULE OF THUMB VERY QUICKLY...
DRESS THE BABY ACCORDING TO HOW YOU FEEL, PLUS
ONE LIGHT BLANKET...UNLESS THE BABY'S
GRANDMOTHER IS AROUND. THEN YOU ADD
TWO MORE BLANKETS AND A SNOWSUIT.

...BUT HE DOESN'T EAT A THING!

DADDY, MOMMY'S STOMACH IS STILL FAT.
DOES SHE HAVE ANY MORE PEOPLE IN THERE?

THE EASTER BUNNY COMES DOWN THE CHIMNEY JUST
LIKE SANTA CLAUS AND HE RIDES IN AN EASTER CART
PULLED BY EIGHT CHICKENS. BUT HE DOESN'T SAY
"HO, HO, HO" CAUSE RABBITS CAN'T TALK.

THIS YOUNG LADY WAS ADOPTED FROM HONG KONG
WHEN SHE WAS A BABY, AMELIA, AND SHE
SPEAKS ENGLISH SO WELL!

MINE!            MINE!

YOU LOOKED TIRED WHEN I CAME HOME FROM WORK TODAY. HOW WAS YOUR DAY?
KISS
OH, ..TYPICAL. LET'S SEE, I DID SIX LOADS OF LAUNDRY, GAVE THE DOG A FLEA BATH, BAKED TWO DOZEN CUPCAKES FOR THE KINDERGARDEN BAKE SALE, REMOVED A SPLINTER FROM KYLE'S THUMB AND A NOODLE FROM RYAN'S NOSE, FILLED IN FOR JENNY'S MOTHER AT THE BROWNIE MEETING, AND SAVED THE CAT FROM BEING FLUSHED DOWN THE TOILET... NOTHING UNUSUAL...
YAWN
...GOODNIGHT HONEY.
GOODNIGHT.